Book 3

By John Holzmann
Illustrated by Dave Lilly

Published by
Avyx, Inc.
8032 South Grant Way
Littleton, CO 80122-2705
(303) 483-0140 FAX (303) 483-0141
E-Mail: info@avyx.com

ISBN 978-1-887840-47-7

Table of Contents

Lesson 17

A Fast Swim 1
A Bum Leg 3
Swim for It 5
What Bit Dan? 7
Does Dan or Stan Win? 9

Lesson 18

The Tent* 12
A Hint* 15
A Cast* 17
The Fish* 19
Fish and Chips* 21

Lesson 19

The Camp Test 23
The Pump Test 26
The Tramp Test 28
The Stamp Box 30
Where is Bill? 32

Lesson 20

The Best Boat 34
Boat Two 36
A Big Wind 39
Back to the Shop 41
How About a Raft? 44

Lesson 21

The Raft Trip 46
Can We Eat? 48
Wet Buns? 50
An Unstuck Raft? 52
A Good Day? 55

Lesson 22

Rolf Plays Golf 57
Scott's Hit 59
In the Pond 61
Rolf's Best Hit 63
A Duck Ball? 65

Lesson 23

Mo Plays Spy 68
A Pal 70
What Is That? 72
In the Mud 74
Fred Gets Mo 77

Lesson 24

The Bake Sale 80
The Prune Cake 82
The Mix Fizzes 84
Black Smoke 86
A Good Cake 89

* By Duane Bolin

"The man who doesn't

read good books

has no advantage over the man

who can't read them."

— Mark Twain

A Fast Swim

Stan and Dan are twins who swim fast. They are glad to test who is best.

Stan and Dan go to a pond to swim. Stan says to Dan, “I bet you can’t swim to that rock as fast as I can.”

“What?” asks Dan. “That rock out there?”

→

who

Stan says, “Yes. I bet you can’t get there as fast as I can.”

“I bet I can!” says Dan.

“Good luck,” says Stan, and he jumps in the pond.

Dan jumps in, too. “See you there!” he says.

Stan swims next to him.

A Bum Leg

The two lads swim and swim.

Stan is just a bit back of Dan.

Dan yells, “Ow! Ow! Help!”

“What did you do?” yells Stan.

He swims up next to Dan.

“It’s my leg!” says Dan. “I have been bit!”

been

"Where?" asks Stan.

"On my leg! Here!" says Dan. He has his hand on his leg. But it is too black in the pond. Stan can not see Dan's leg.

"I can not see your leg," Stan says. "Can you lift it up?"

"No way!" says Dan. "Oh, what will we do?!"

Swim for It

As Dan swims, he yells. He says he has been bitten. He grabs his leg. “What will we do?” he asks his twin, Stan.

“Swim to the land,” says Stan.

“But if I swim, I will have to let go!” says Dan. “And what if the thing that bit me does it again?”

again

"Just swim!" says Stan.

"But I can't swim unless I let go!"

"So let go!" Stan says.

"But if I let go . . ."

"Do not think, 'What if.' Just let go and swim!" Stan says.

Dan knows he must get back to land. He lets go of his leg and swims. Stan is at his back to help him if things go bad.

What Bit Dan?

The lads get to land. Dan looks at his leg. "Wow!" he says. "Look at that! I have been bit bad."

"What do you think bit you?" asks Stan.

"A croc?" says Dan.

"A croc is too big. And your cuts are too small. There are no crocs in this pond!" says Stan.

wow seen fish like

Dan admits he has not seen a croc in the pond. "So, then, was it a fish?" he asks.

"There are no fish in this pond that could have bit you like that!" says Stan.

"Then I do not know what bit me," says Dan. "And now, I bet, I will get sick."

Does Dan or Stan Win?

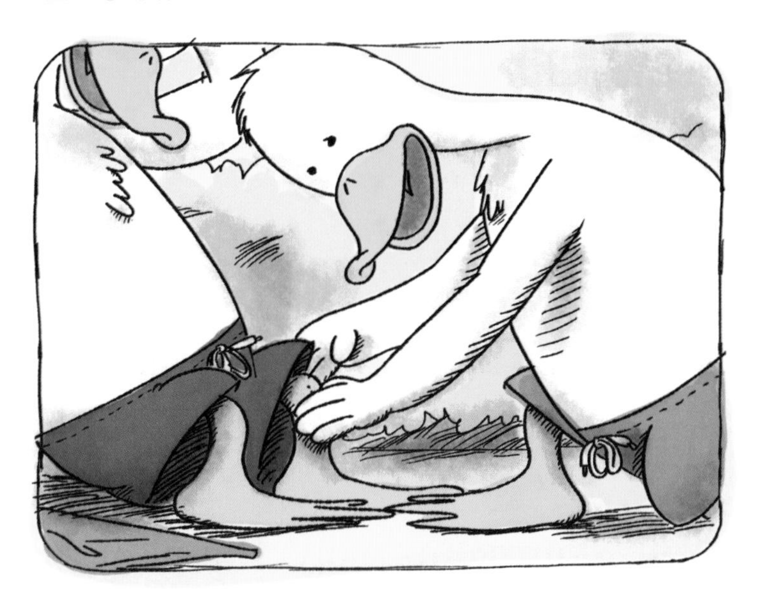

Was Dan bit by a croc or a fish?

Dan says, “Maybe I was not bit. Maybe I hit a stick. Could I have hit a stick that had two twigs or stems?”

“I see a bit of twig stuck in your leg,” says Stan.

maybe

"You do?" says Dan. "Can you get it out for me?"

"Let's see," says Stan.

He grabs the stem and it comes out. He looks at the spot where the stem was.

"The skin seems okay. I think it was just a small prick."

The two lads sit a bit, then swim again. Stan wins on the way to the rock. Dan wins on the way back. Dan says. “It is best when two can win. I am glad you are my twin.”

“Me, too,” says Stan.

The Tent

Greg is a lad.

Gramps is Greg's granddad.

"I am sad," says Greg. "I have nothing to do."

Gramps says, "Let us go camp in the hills. That will be fun for you!"

"Yes!" yells Greg. "To camp in the hills will be grand."

"Help me with the tent, Greg," says Gramps. "Lend me a hand." Greg and Gramps fuss with the tent, but they can not get it up.

Gramps says, "Let us rest a bit. Can you get me a drink in a cup?" Greg gets Gramps a drink and they sit and sip from their cups. Just then, a gust of wind fills the tent up.

Greg says, “If we trap the wind in the tent, it will help us set the tent up!”

So Greg runs to clamp the tent shut.

And in less than a wink, Greg has the tent set up.

A Hint

Gramps and Greg got the tent up.

"Can we get some grub now?"

Greg asks.

"Yes," says Gramps. "We must."

"Did you pack snacks?" asks

Greg.

Gramps says, "No, I did not. But

we will get some on a quest."

"Where will we go?" asks Greg.

Gramps says, "To the pond in the west."

Greg asks, "How can that be?"

"I will give you a hint," says Gramps. "Then you will see."

"The grub has fins," says Gramps, "and the grub has gills."

"So," says Greg, "we will cast for fish in the pond in the hills!"

A Cast

Greg and Gramps cast for grub
with fins and gills.
"What a lot of fun, Gramps," says
Greg. "You are the best."
He gives Gramps a hug and tugs
at his vest.
"Cast to the west," says Gramps.
"Then let your rod rest. The fish
will come if you just let it be!"

flash

So Greg casts to the west and lets his rod be, but it does not tip as best as he can see.

In a flash, Greg's rod dips just a bit. He grabs for it, but lets it slip. Gramps grabs for Greg's rod, too, but into the pond it flips!

"I will get it!" Greg yells, as he stands to jump in.

"Do not jump!" yells Gramps, as he wags his hand at him.

The Fish

"Gramps!" yells Greg. "My rod will be lost."

"You can trust me, my lad. Your rod is not lost," says Gramps. "I'll use this net." And he gives it a toss.

"Blast that fish!" Greg thinks. But Gramps says, "Lend me a hand."

Greg helps Gramps bring in the net. And they set it in the sand.

The end of the net comes up with a bump.

In the net is Greg's rod . . . and a lump that jumps!

But it is not a lump! It is a big fish.

Gramps claps his hands. And Greg does a big fish jig.

Fish and Chips

Greg and Gramps trot back to the tent. The sun will go in a bit.

"Greg, grab a lamp for us," says Gramps. "We will snack by it."

Gramps skins the big fish.

"This trip is a blast," says Greg.

He gets drinks, cups, and a dish.

Gramps drops the fish in a pan.

chips

He flips it with a twist.

“It smells good!” says Greg.

Gramps says, “With fish, we must have chips.”

“We must!” says Greg. He grins and smacks his lips.

Gramps and Greg fed on fish and chips till the sun was red.

They gabbed till they went to bed.

The Camp Test

Ned and Zack are at the West Bunk Camp. There are ten lads in their tent. All ten lads do tests of skill.

The lads run out of camp and up a hill. At the top, there is a big log that goes over a pit.

over

The lads must run across the log and not fall off. It is not a big drop, but the lads do not want to fall.

If a lad falls off, he must get out of the pit and do it again until he can run and not fall.

All the lads must run across the log. Then all the lads can go on to the next test.

Just one lad, Jim, falls in. He jumps out and runs again. And again. And again.

Jim is hot when he runs across the log and does not fall.

The Pump Test

When Jim gets across the log, the lads just want to rest. But they must do the rest of the tests. They come to a pump.

Ten jugs stand at the pump.

All ten lads must fill a jug.

All the lads pump and pump. But the water does not come.

water

The lads are hot.

"Should we quit?" asks Bill.

Not one lad wants to pump again.

"I think the water will come,"

Nick says as he pumps.

And then the water comes.

"Yes!" all the lads yell.

They have a drink and get wet.

They have been so hot, they are

glad to be wet.

The Tramp Test

The next test is a tramp.

The lads must get on the tramp, one by one, jump one jump, and then get off.

Jim does not stop at one jump. So Nick gets on as Jim still jumps. And Jim's last jump dumps Nick off!

It can be bad if you fall off. But Nick is okay.

One lad jumps four jumps on the tramp when he should jump just one.

Two lads jump three jumps.

So the test is not as fast as it could be. And the lads yell and bump their pals a bit. But they have fun.

The Stamp Box

Next, the lads must hunt for a box with a nest on it. The box has a stamp and an ink pad in it. All of the lads must stamp their hand. Then they can run back to camp. When all of them get back, the lads know they will get something good. So they go fast.

path down

As they go down the path, the lads look for the box. Is it in a plant? On a stump? Under a clump of moss? Should they look up? Or down? Where is it?

Dan thinks he sees the nest.

Dan goes over to look.

It is what he wants.

He yells, "Lads! Here is the stamp!"

Where is Bill?

The lads stamp their hands and run to camp. But not Bill. Bill sits down. When Bill does not come into camp, Zack and Jim go to get him.

When Zack sees him, he says, “Come on, Bill!”

“I can’t,” Bill says. “My leg has a cramp in it!”

walk

Zack and Jim help Bill walk.

When the three lads walk into camp, the rest of the lads yell, clap, and stomp.

Then comes the best thing yet.

The man that runs the camp has a big pan of buns and jam. Plus, all the lads get a pack of gum. Yum!

Then they sit and tell tall fibs and do not get to bed till one!

(Week 20) 1-12-09

The Best Boat

Brent, Rob, Trent, and Clint go to Grant's Pond. They want to race in two sail boats. A man at the pond rents boats. Brent and Rob will rent a boat. And Trent and Clint will rent one, too.

Trent and Clint stop to look at the pond. Brent and Rob go to the

boat race sail

shop to ask if they can rent a sail boat for a race.

“Oh!” says the man. “I have just the craft for you. It is fast!”

“That is what we want,” says Rob.

“What does it cost to rent?” asks Brent.

“Ten bucks,” says the man.

“Okay,” says Rob. “We want it.”

Boat Two

Rob and Brent rent the best boat.

Then Trent and Clint go to the shop.

Clint asks the man, “Do you have a sail boat we can rent?”

“I do,” says the man. “It will cost you six bucks.”

Brent is mad. The man said it would cost him *ten* bucks to rent a boat. But now he says it will cost Clint and Trent just *six*!

Brent is about to say something when Rob grabs him and says, "Do not say a thing! Yes, we will pay ten bucks and →

they will pay just six. But we got the best boat. We can win with our fast boat."

So the lads rent their boats. Then they go down to the dock and rig the boats to sail.

"Cast off!" says Rob.

They will race.

A Big Wind

The lads are on the pond when a gust of wind comes that wafts their sails aloft. Brent and Rob's boat is swift. It jets past Trent and Clint's boat.

Then, a big gust hits. The lads hear a crack! The mast on the fast boat snaps. It bonks Rob on the ear. Rob grunts as the mast and the sail drop on him! →

Brent, Clint and Trent rip at the sail to get it off Rob.

Rob's pals get the mast and the sail off of him. But Rob has a big welt and a lump on his ear.

"Look at the lump swell!"

"Let's set a wet rag on it," says Brent.

Trent grabs his sock, dumps it in the pond, and plants it on Rob's ear.

Back to the Shop

Brent looks at the mast and gasps.

"Look at that! It's bent! From a gust of wind?!"

"How can we get back?" he says.

"With no sail, our boat is stuck."

done

"You grab that end of my belt, and I will grab this end. We can drag you," says Clint. And that is what they do.

When the lads get back to the dock, the boat man is upset. "What did you do?" he asks. He thinks they bent the mast.

"It was not us," says Brent. "It just fell. A gust of wind was too big. One sec we are okay and the next, the mast falls. See? It hit Rob on the ear."

"You must have done something," says the man.

"No," say the lads. "We had just cast off. The wind bent the mast so it fell."

How About a Raft?

The boat man tells the lads they do not have to pay rent for the boat.

"Good! We should not have to pay." says Brent. "That mast fell when we had been out for just a bit. Clint and Trent had to drag us back."

shall

“Do you want to go back out, then?” asks the man.

Clint asks, “Do you have a big raft that all of us can rest on?”

“I do!” says the man. “The raft costs six bucks—what your boat cost.”

“Shall we do it?” asks Clint.

His pals nod.

“Well, then, let’s go!” says Clint.

The Raft Trip

Brent, Rob, Trent, and Clint get on the raft. The raft costs six bucks. But the cost is not bad. And all of them can get on.

Rob gets on the raft, sits down, and then rests on his back. He lets the rest of the lads sail the raft.

The raft drifts across the pond. It is not swift. So, in a bit, all the lads rest on their backs. They look up and think and gab.

On a raft, you do not have to do a thing. So the lads sit and drift. And the sun gives them a tan. The lads think it is fun to drift on their raft.

Can We Eat?

Clint says. “It’s one! Let’s eat!”

Brent looks in the bag. “We have some buns with ham and 7-Up®.”

The lads are about to eat. But then Rob says, “Oh, no! Do you see where we are?”

The wind has sent them to drift by a spit of sand. Tufts of grass and plants stick up.

Rob yells, "We are about to hit!"

Then the raft hits a rock and tips.

One end is up on the rock, and

one is down in the pond.

And then the bag of buns falls

into the pond!

Brent sees the bag fall, but he

cannot grab it. He yells, "Clint!

Grab the buns! They fell in the

pond!"

Wet Buns?

Clint grabs the buns out of the pond and lifts them from the bag. The lads are glad just one is wet. They still have food to eat. They thank God for food that is not wet. And then they eat. But Rob thinks, "How do we get out of here?" One end of the raft is on the rock, and it is stuck in muck and grass.

After they eat, the lads get off the raft. They can tell they are in a bad spot.

Brent and Rob stand on the land where the raft is stuck.

Clint and Trent swim to the end of the raft that is still in the pond.

The lads grab the raft and tug.

But it will not come off the rock.

An Unstuck Raft

The lads huff and puff to get the raft off the rock. But the raft will not come off.

Then Brent yells, “Ow! Ants are in my pants!” As he says this, he slaps his pants and jumps in the pond.

right

When he jumps, a swell rocks the raft a bit. The lads hear the raft clunk on the rock.

Then Clint yells, "I have it! I know how to get us off the rock! Two of us should jump in the pond. The swell will lift the raft. If two of us ram the raft as the swell lifts it, I think we can get the raft off the rock!"

“I think he is right!” says Rob.
“Brent and Clint, you can jump in and Trent and I can ram the raft.”
They do that and the raft comes off the rock.

A Good Day?

As they go back to the boat shop, Brent says, "It was no fun when the ants got in my pants. And I am sad the mast hit you, Rob. But this trip has been a blast! I am glad the man at the boat shop let us have this raft."

Clint grins and says, "What a crack-up to see you slap your pants when ants are in them!"

day

Brent grins, too. “Maybe you should have some ants in *your* pants and see how it is!”

And with that, Trent, Rob, and Clint jump on Brent and they all fall into the pond.

The lads get back to the dock as the sun is about to set.

“Did you have a good day?” asks the man.

All the lads say, “Yes!”

Rolf Plays Golf

Rolf wants to hit golf balls in the Swiss Alps. The Alps are big hills that slant up and have big cliffs. Rolf goes up into the Alps. He has golf balls and golf clubs. His best bud, Scott, goes with him. Rolf drops a ball on the top of an Alp. He hits it with his club to see if he can hit it into a pond all the way down the hill. →

Rolf hits the ball. It goes all the way down the hill. But it goes a bit to the left. It misses the pond. It lands on the tin top of a hut. A dog in the grass next to the hut jumps up and barks.

"That was a good hit," says Scott. "But I am glad you did not hit that dog!"

Scott's Hit

"Do you want to hit a ball?" Rolf asks Scott.

"That would be fun," says Scott. "Can I hit one into the pond?"

"I bet you can," says Rolf. "If you hit it well, it will go in the pond. Just do not hit it to the left."

The lads hear a yell from the hut that the ball hit.

were

A man yells, "You lads had best not hit my hut again!"

"Sorry!" yells Rolf.

The man goes back in his hut.

Scott hits the ball. It slants to the left just as Rolf's ball did. It does not get to the pond or hit the hut. It hits a nest. (It is good there were no eggs in it!)

In the Pond

Rolf drops a ball and hits it with zest. It is a small speck when it drops into the pond.

It is the best shot yet.

"That was good," says Scott.

"But you can not hit a ball as well as I can."

"Go for it!" says Rolf. He hands Scott the club and steps back.

far whack splash

Whack!

The lads look at the ball. They see a splash. Scott's ball is way past where Rolf's ball hit.

"Wow!" says Scott. "Did you see that?! That was grand!"

"Yep," says Rolf. He is a bit mad. "I will hit one so far you will not see where it lands."

Rolf's Best Hit

Scott drops a ball for Rolf to hit. Rolf looks at it. "That is my best ball. If I hit it well, it will go all the way past the pond."

He hits it, but a bit off. The ball hits a rock and then plops in the pond.

"Here," says Scott. "Hit it again."

Rolf grabs the ball Scott hands him. "This ball is as good as the last," Rolf says. "If I hit it well, it will go far."

He hits it. Crack! It is a good hit. It looks as if the ball will go all the way past the pond. He grins at Scott.

But Scott says, "See that duck? I think it got the ball in its bill."

A Duck Ball?

The duck flaps by the lads. It has a ball in its bill! As the duck passes the lads, it drops the ball and quacks.

"Thanks a lot!" says Rolf.

"It's your ball all right!" says Scott.

Rolf picks it up and looks at it. “I do not get this. A duck with my ball in its bill?”

“You must have hit that ball just right to get it in his bill!” says Scott.

“No way!” says Rolf.

“Well, he got it somehow!” says Scott. “You want to hit again?”

"No," says Rolf. "I think I will quit. I have seen all I want!"

"Me, too," says Scott.

The lads go back down the hill.

And they have lots of things to discuss!

Mo Plays Spy

Mo is ten. He plays spy. He plays a spry spy. He can run fast, jump, and kick. He can bend any way you could think. He can hit with his fist. He can do all the things a good spy can do. But one day this stuff does not help him.

Mo is out for a walk. He sees a lad with a yo-yo.

play

Mo grins and says, “Hi! I bet your yo-yo is a blast to play with.”

“It is!” says the lad.

Mo cannot think of a thing to add.

So he says, “Well, see you!”

The yo-yo lad goes on, but Mo thinks to himself, “It would be good to get to know him. When I see him again, I will ask him if he wants to play ball!”

A Pal

The next day Mo is out for a walk. He bumps into the yo-yo lad again.

"Hi," he says. "Do you want to play some ball?"

"That would be grand!" says the lad. "By the way," he says, "I am Fred."

"And I am Mo," says Mo.

The two lads slap hands.

Then they get a ball, a bat, and two mitts, and they go to play.

"Who should bat?" asks Fred.

"If you want to, that is okay with me," says Mo.

Fred hits the ball. Mo gets it and passes it back to Fred.

What Is That?

Mo and Fred hit and toss a ball.

Then Mo sees an odd thing in the sky. Mo cannot tell what it is. He looks up. Fred looks up, too.

Mo asks, "What is that?"

Fred says, "It looks like bees!

Can you hear it? It buzzes.

It *is* bees!"

bee	new	time

"Bees!?" says Mo. "It must be a lot of bees to look like that! They will come here. Let's run!"

"You do not have to run!" says Fred. "They want a new nest. They will not bug us."

To get the bees away, Mo runs and jumps and kicks. But he does all of them at one time!

In the Mud

Fred sees Mo run, jump, and kick.

Fred thinks Mo looks daft. “Come back!” he yells.

But Mo does not come back.

Fred goes to see where the bees go.

At last Mo stops and looks back. “Well,” says Mo to himself, “if Fred wants to be bitten, that is up to him. But I do not like bees!” Mo runs to the pond. He plans to jump into the pond so the bees can’t get him.

But there is mud on the bank of the pond. Mo slips and falls flat in the mud! What a mess! He has a lot of mud on him!

Is he sad about the mud? No! He thinks, “If I sit in the mud, the bees will not see me. And they will not smell me. The bees will let me be.”

Fred Gets Mo

Fred goes to the pond. He sees Mo in the mud.

Fred plans a bit of fun. He fills his cap with water and dumps it on Mo!

Mo jumps up. He is mad!

He runs at Fred and yells, "Let me be! I do not want the bees to know where I am!" →

Fred says. "The bees do not want to know where you are! They just want a new nest."

The lads stand for a bit.

At last, Mo says, "A bee bit me when I was small. If I get bit by bees, it is bad for me."

"Sorry," says Fred. "I did not know." Then he says, "Would you like to play ball again?"

"Okay!" says Mo.

He is about to walk back when Fred grins. “You want to play like that?” asks Fred.

“Like what?” says Mo.

“Look at yourself,” says Fred.

Mo looks at himself.

“Maybe you should swim and then play ball,” says Fred.

Mo grins as he jumps in the pond.

The Bake Sale

Jane and Kate talk about the Kids Club bake sale. The sale will make funds for kids who have no homes.

Jane and Kate want to help the kids and win a prize, too. For the best cake, the prize is two sets of skates.

talk

"Let's make my date and prune glaze cake!" says Jane.

"Prunes?!" says Kate. "I hate prunes!"

"But you will love this cake," says Jane. "It has a bit of Coke® in it that makes it fizz and adds a bit of a bite. Yum!"

"Oh! And the glaze! The glaze is to die for!"

The Prune Cake

Jane says the glaze on her prune cake is "to die for."

"Well," says Kate. "I don't want to die for this cake. But I will help you make one. I will try some. And if I like it, I will help you make a new cake for the bake sale. Or, if I don't like it, can we make a cake that I like?"

oven

"That will be fine with me!" says Jane. "But you will love my cake!"

"Okay," says Kate.

The two gals go to Jane's home. They get the things they need. Jane fires up the oven. "It has to be hot when we set the cake in," she says.

The Mix Fizzes

As the oven gets hot, the gals cut the prunes, dates, and some nuts. They mix all the things. Then they dump a cup of Coke® on top. The stuff fizzes.

"Yuck!" says Kate. "It looks like glop!"

"But you will love it!" says Jane.

finger

She sticks her finger in and licks it off. She smiles a big smile. “Yum! Try it!”

“But it does not look good to me!” says Kate. But she sticks her finger into the mix, then licks a bit off. “Hmm!” she says. “It’s not too bad!”

Jane grins. “You will like it more when we bake it.”

Then Kate sees smoke.

Black Smoke

Kate sees smoke. It comes from the oven. “What is that?” she asks Jane.

“What?” says Jane as she looks at the oven. “Oh, no! I did not look in the oven when I lit it!”

When she looks, she sees that she left a plate inside the oven. The plate had spills from the last time the oven was on. Now the spills are black, and smoke comes out of them!

Jane grabs a hot pad and a mitt. She lifts the plate from the oven.

The thick fumes make the gals want to cry!

"Get that outside!" says Kate.

Jane sets the plate on the deck.

"It was a good thing there were no flames or fire!" says Kate.

The gals wave their hands to get the smoke out of the house.

A Good Cake

When the smoke is out of the oven, the gals set the cake inside to bake.

It bakes for some time. Then Jane takes a pick and pokes the top of the cake. The cake does not fall.

"It's done!" she says.

judge

Jane takes the cake from the oven. After they make the glaze, the gals try the cake. It is good. In fact, Kate loves it. “Shall we make one for the sale?” she asks. “You bet!” says Jane. And so they do.

When they take their cake to the contest, the judges do not love it like the gals do.

The gals do not win.

But the cake sells well. And that is good!

The Kids Club gets the funds it needs to get a home.

The gals had fun when they made the cake. And Kate now knows what cake she likes best!

I *Did* Read It!

This Certificate of Completion
is hereby granted to

Sam Hahn
____

to certify completion of

I Can Read It!

Book 3

Mom
____
Presented by

2-10-09
____
Date